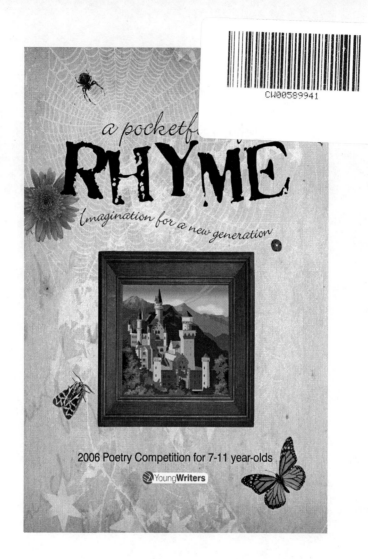

a pocketful of

RHYME

Imagination for a new generation

2006 Poetry Competition for 7-11 year-olds

Co Durham Vol II
Edited by Allison Dowse

 Young**Writers**

First published in Great Britain in 2006 by:
Young Writers
Remus House
Coltsfoot Drive
Peterborough
PE2 9JX
Telephone: 01733 890066
Website: www.youngwriters.co.uk

SB ISBN 1 84602 468 4

Foreword

Young Writers was established in 1991 and has been passionately devoted to the promotion of reading and writing in children and young adults ever since. The quest continues today. Young Writers remains as committed to the nurturing of poetic and literary talent as ever.

This year's Young Writers competition has proven as vibrant and dynamic as ever and we are delighted to present a showcase of the best poetry from across the UK and in some cases overseas. Each poem has been selected from a wealth of *A Pocketful Of Rhyme* entries before ultimately being published in this, our fourteenth primary school poetry series.

Once again, we have been supremely impressed by the overall quality of the entries we have received. The imagination, energy and creativity which has gone into each young writer's entry made choosing the poems a challenging and often difficult but ultimately hugely rewarding task - the general high standard of the work submitted ensured this opportunity to bring their poetry to a larger appreciative audience.

We sincerely hope you are pleased with this final collection and that you will enjoy *A Pocketful Of Rhyme Co Durham Vol II* for many years to come.

Contents

Ryan Cooper (9)   37
Charlotte Elizabeth Bailey (9)   38
Jack Emberson (9)   39
Caitlin Neasham (9)   40
Alex Hendry (9)   41
Katya Chetina (9)   42
Kate Appleton (7)   43
James Borland (8)   44
Katherine Bradshaw (7)   45
Martin Briggs (7)   46
Sarah Brown (7)   47
Lewis Elliot Dawe (7)   48
Gradey Fairburn (7)   49
Gavin Fraser (8)   50
Laura Greenley (8)   51
Eleanor Griffin (8)   52
Katie Harrington (8)   53
Toni Hendry (8)   54
Ellie Jayne Hopgood (8)   55
Ewan Loftus (7)   56
Kqia Lomas (7)   57
Rebekah Lumsdon (8)   58
Georgia McCormick (8)   59
Freya Patterson (7)   60
Isla Readman (7)   61
Jake Robson (7)   62
Sven Lars Signer (7)   63
Alex Thornton (7)   64
Lucy Traynor (7)   65
Kaitlin Walton (7)   66
Benjamin White (8)   67

Shotton Primary School
Lauren Wilcox (8)   68
Connor Simpson (8)   69
Leigh Patterson (9)   70
James Seaton (9)   71
Jennifer Scott (8)   72
Conor Willetts (9)   73
Craig Adey (9)   74
Ben Bowes (9)   75

Matthew Peart (10)   119
Jasmine Sanderson (9)   120
Hannah Tones (9)   121
Emily Blenkinsopp (9)   122
Danielle Bartram (10)   123

Startforth CE Primary School
Harry Day (10)   124
Sandra-Lee Prewitt (11)   125
Ellen Ritchie (10)   126
Zoe Nicholson (10)   127
Christopher Ridgway (10)   128
Christopher Wood (9)   129
Aaron North (11)   130
Emily Knox (11)   131
Jack Robinson (10)   132
Becky McKitton & Jaymie Hartley (11)   133
Emilie Riley (10)   134
Christopher Rutter (11)   135
Alex Doyle (10)   136
Emily Carey & Emily Kell (11)   137
James Harrison (11)   138
Matthew Heron (10)   139
Fred Bowron (10)   140

Wingate Junior School
Roy Stephenson (8)   141
Natalie Clish (8)   142
Jennifer Wilkinson (9)   143
Adam Churchman (8)   144
Jordan Bostock (8)   145
Jordanna Simpson (8)   146
Melissa O'Neill (8)   147
Jason Robson (8)   148
Craig Whiting (9)   149
Shaunie Leigh (8)   150
Daniel Healer (9)   151
Adam Presho (7)   152
Adam Leonard (8)   153
Aimee Atkinson (9)   154
Luke Catleugh (8)   155

The Poems

Chickenpox

My brother's got lots of spots,
It's like a giant dot-to-dot.
I'm tempted to get my pen
And write numbers from one to ten.
My mum put on some calamine cream,
It made him look like a ghost from a dream.
Now he's better we're jumping for joy,
As now he's no longer a spotty boy.

Tegan Stevenson (11)
Dodmire Junior School

Steam Train

Rushing along the metal tracks
Through the gloomy tunnel
Clashing
Clanging
Whizzing past the station
In the blink of an eye
Swaying from side to side
As it hurtles along
Zooming past like a cheetah
Then coming to a halt with a shriek and a screech.

Jason Watt (9)
Dodmire Junior School

Steam Train

Clickety clack
The steam train swaying from side to side
Rushing like a rocket
The rails creaking
As it rumbles like a huge iron dragon
Whistling through the gloomy, dark tunnel
Then whooshing past the stations
With the puffing steam billowing like clouds
Screeching to a halt at the station
Starting yet again
Huffing and puffing like a huge sigh
Before disappearing into the depths
Of another deep tunnel.

Rajan Singh Bura (10)
Dodmire Junior School

Steam Train

Rushing
Whizzing
Screeching
Howling
Parents shouting
Children crying
The fireman sweating
Tunnel looming
Train puffing
Rails creaking
Whistles hooting
Train halting
Journey ending.

James Alexander Reese (10)
Dodmire Junior School

Steam Train

The train's swaying from side to side
On the shining tracks
Luggage tipping over as the train rumbles along
Sounding like a battle far away
Steam boiling into the sky
Rattles, squeaks and rumbles
As the brain clatters by.

Chloe Buxton (9)
Dodmire Junior School

Steam Train

The train goes whizzing down the rusty track
Then it's swallowed up in a deep, dark tunnel.
Firemen working their socks off.
Rails going creak, creak, creak.
Stopping at the station in a cloud of steam,
Whistling 'Hi!' to folks on the way.

Liam Bonner (10)
Dodmire Junior School

Steam Train

Swaying from side to side
The steam train goes whizzing down the track
It comes to an abrupt halt at the station
Then sets off to its next destination
Clattering down the old, rusty track
Rumbling and rattling
The huge, black, iron monster whooshing
Through a tunnel
With white clouds of steam puffing out
Like an angry dragon's breath.

Joshua Ward (10)
Dodmire Junior School

Steam Train

There's a wind
From the train passing by
Faster than a car,
Faster than a bird,
The big, heavy, iron giant
Rocking from side to side,
The rattle, clatter and creaking of the rails
As it rumbles out of the dark and gloomy tunnel
To reach its destination up ahead.

Ryan Sung (10)
Dodmire Junior School

Steam Train

The train goes by
With a clatter and a clitter
Rattling side by side
People jolt when it comes to a halt
The train is a squeaking, squealing giant
Whizzing along as if charging into battle
Whistling
Rumbling like thunder
And screeching
That's the way the train goes by.

Johnson Hunter (9)
Dodmire Junior School

Steam Train

The metal monster roars
At all the passers-by
His round bright light shines in the tunnel
He gives out a piercing shriek
At the station
Then rumbles like thunder along the metal tracks
Whizzing past houses and fences
With a creak and a rattle
A whistle and a clatter
Halting with a puff of smoke
As the wheels jolt into the next station
And the brakes squeal.

Daniel Robson (10)
Dodmire Junior School

Seasons

Spring is the first season of the year.
When the flowers and buds bloom and grow
I think the fairies put them there a long time ago
In summer you have lots of fun
And have a picnic maybe with a sticky bun
In autumn the leaves fall off the trees
All different colours good enough to please
Winter gets really cold with Christmas on the way
And New Year's Day.

Laura Kate Szymanski (8)
Dodmire Junior School

Trains

Train black, train grey, over the hills and far away
Whizzing past like a plane in the sky
You can see it, so can I
Train blue, train green, fastest train I've ever seen
Moving along on a metal track
Driving forward, driving back, I can see it
Going over the hills when we go past.

Georgia Copeland (8)
Dodmire Junior School

Steam Train

Rumble tumbling
Thundering steam train
Charging as if into battle
Taking up its position in the station
Whistling and squeaking
Taking on water
To make a big puff of steam.

Carl Alderson (9)
Dodmire Junior School

Steam Train

Through the countryside the train clatters
Past roads and trees and houses
Rattling along the rails
As the coal is shovelled into the fire-box
To make the engine work
Speeding through the dark tunnel
Round the turns
And then along the straight
With a sharp whistle blowing
And the steam billowing
Till the brakes are pulled on with a screech
And people get off and on at the station.

Robert Black (9)
Dodmire Junior School

Smells

My uncle smells of strawberry.
My father smells of lime.
My mother smells of orange.
My auntie smells of wine.

My grandad smells of pickles.
My grandma smells of lard.
My cousin smells of lemon.
The dog smells of the yard.

My sister smells of carrots.
My brother smells of rice.
The cat smells of cabbage
And I smell very nice!

Chloe Lewis (8)
Dodmire Junior School

The Weather

The clouds in the sky
All fluffy and white
Float around all snowy and high
Catch one and it feels so light.
The wind rustles loudly
The leaves fall aground
They sigh so soundly
And they sing all around.
The thunder it bangs
The lightning it strikes
It sounds like it sang
But people do not like.
The snow it falls so softly
All crunchy and soft
The sun it shines hotly
And the snow is all lost.
The rain patters down
All soggy and wet
It laughs like a clown
But it does not set.

Toni Jones (11)
Dodmire Junior School

Football Fans

F ans cheering
O n the ball, he's
O n the ball
T eams racing for the ball
B ack of the net it goes
A ll the fans screaming
L egs going faster and faster
L ong goes the ball
  1, 2, 3 goals in the back of the net.

T.jay Leonard (8)
Dodmire Junior School

The Cat Of Cats

I am the cat of cats. I am the everlasting cat!
Cunning and old and sleek as jam,
The everlasting cat!
I hunt the vermin in the night -
The everlasting cat!
For the best without the light -
The everlasting cat!

Elisha Fleming (7)
Dodmire Junior School

Love Poem

Live lives in a rainbow
Love lives in our heart
And she does not like us apart
Love lives in a river
Love lives in everyone
And she never leaves your side
Love lives in your lives
Love lives in a river
She cares for us a lot.

Leighanne Jones (10)
Dodmire Junior School

Murphy and Cyi

On a warm summer's day, all was calm,
When two pups were born on Littlegrove Farm.
The pups were for sale, at such a small price,
'I really would like them Mum, that would be nice.'
Mum agreed and we took them home,
They ran around the garden and chewed on a bone.
Now they are three and I still love them so much,
They are really cute and have such a soft touch.
When it's not raining we like to take them to the park
And when they see squirrels they both like to bark,
Murphy and Cyi always like to play together,
I think they'll be best friends forever.

Simranjit Kaur Chhokar (11)
Dodmire Junior School

My Best Friend

My best friend is really cool,
We hang everywhere not just in school.
We go to the shopping mall
Or just the school hall,
My best friend is really cool.

My best friend is really cool,
We hang everywhere not just in school.
We go roller skating
Or just do painting,
My best friend is really cool.

My best friend is really cool,
We hang everywhere, not just in school.
We go on Sims
Or just sing hymns,
My best friend is really cool.

Ashley Ruddam (11)
Dodmire Junior School

Winter

It's cold and chilly,
Out in the street.
You can hardly move,
With your frozen feet.

There's icicles dangling,
From the branches on the tree,
Shining and glinting,
For me and you to see.

Charlotte Roscoe (10)
Dodmire Junior School

Steam Train

Whizzing train
Creaking and rattling along the rails
Rushing through a pitch-black tunnel
Huffing and puffing
Squeaking and screeching
Rattling and rumbling like thunder
Foggy clouds of steam
As it sways from side to side
Along the gloomy track.

Frances Wrightson (10)
Dodmire Junior School

Steam Train

Rumbling like thunder through the deep, dark tunnel,
Whistling like the wind
And the rails creaking,
The fireman working really hard,
His brow's sweating to get the train moving.
The big black machine swaying from side to side,
Clattering on the track
Like a big angry monster.

Keenan Alexander (9)
Dodmire Junior School

Steam Train

Steam train whizzing out of the tunnel
Like thunder
Smoke like fog
As it comes swiftly to a halt
Then off again through the mist
Rattling along the rails once more
On its way to the next station.

Lucas Wright (9)
Dodmire Junior School

Steam Train

Along the track comes a racing cheetah
    Huffing and puffing
    Shrieking and squeaking
Whistling while it rushes along
    Huffing and puffing
    Shrieking and squeaking
Here comes a tunnel, the lair of a dragon
    Huffing and puffing
    Shrieking and squeaking
Out it roars at the other end
    Huffing and puffing
    Shrieking and squeaking
There's a station up ahead
    Huffing and puffing
    Shrieking and squeaking
Rumble, jolt, rest for a minute
    Huffing and puffing
    Shrieking and squeaking
Off again to continue the journey
    Huffing and puffing
    Shrieking and squeaking.

Victoria Monk (10)
Dodmire Junior School

Steam Train

Rushing through the dark gloomy tunnel,
Shrieking out the other end.
Passengers looking amazed at the speed it goes by,
The metal monster rumbling along,
Clattering past like a bolting spark of lightning,
Huffing and puffing, whistling and sparking,
Before screeching to a halt in the station.

Nathan Price (9)
Dodmire Junior School

My Two Brothers

My two brothers drive me up the wall,
My two brothers are very tall.

My two brothers are so annoying,
Everything they get they start destroying.

My two brothers are very sweaty,
My two brothers hate confetti.

But deep down inside they love me to bits,
Even though they have hissy fits.

Gemma Nichol-Brown (11)
Dodmire Junior School

Light To Dark

Light to dark
Dark to light
Stars will twinkle
Till morning light

When birds awake
And the sun shines brighter
We stretch and yawn
On that morning light

When night-time comes
Our sleep awaits
We know our night
Will turn to light

Light to dark
Dark to light.

Megan Wolfe (10)
Dodmire Junior School

Wildlife

W atching wildlife on TV
  I nsects, animals and
  L ife in front of me
D igging up worms that's what kids do best
L ife is everywhere on our planet
  I n gardens and in the countryside
F orgetting life is impossible
E verywhere there are different animals
    I love every one.

Alanna Stevenson (9)
Dodmire Junior School

Steam Train

The steam train hurtles by
Saying, 'Hi,' to all the folks along the way,
Tooting and whistling,
Steam and smoke puffing out.
As it comes to a stop at the station,
Brakes creak and squeal.
Then zooming along again
Like a huge iron monster.
Its light lost as it enters
The gloomy dark of the long, deep tunnel.
A thunderous rumble
As it darts out the other end
Into the bright sunlight
To rattle along the track once more.

Aron Stranks (10)
Dodmire Junior School

My Brothers

My brothers
Are like no others,
One's smart
And one's good at art.

One's in Year 10,
The other's got a great pen,
One made a foot,
The other stayed put.

One's got a great friend,
The other drives me round the bend,
My brother's got a big brown bear,
The other's just got lots of hair.

Emilie van der Gucht (9)
Finchale Primary School

Smoke Animals

S nakes are silly
M onkeys are mischievous
O ctopi are ocean animals
K angaroos are cuddly
E agles are elegant.

A nts are very small
N its are very small
I guanas can camouflage
M ice are small
A nteaters are big
L ions are very big
S nails are small!

Rhiannon Potter (9)
Finchale Primary School

Ghosts

Sleepy monster
Scary and daring
Lurking around at night
Squishy and belchy
Loud and squelchy
I will give you a fright
Strong and transparent
Silly and weird

What am I?

A ghost.

Adam John (9)
Finchale Primary School

Ghosts!

Hello ghost
How much do you boast?
You scared me
Like I was a little pea
I jumped out of my skin
Even though I am thin
Even though you're clear
Everybody can hear
You hide in my shoe
Then you say *boo!*

Reiss Cullen (9)
Finchale Primary School

My Brother Jake

My brother Jake
Really loves to eat cake,
He really is football mad,
He sometimes makes me sad.

He really isn't quite tall,
But kicks the football against the garage wall,
But he's my brother and I love him.

Joshua Luke Renwick (9)
Finchale Primary School

Leaves Are Falling From The Sky

Leaves are red
Leaves are brown
Leaves are crunchy
Leaves float
Some leaves are soggy
Some leaves are fun to jump in
leaves float around trees.

Ryan Cooper (9)
Finchale Primary School

Oh, Mousey

Oh mousey, Oh mousey, let's go to the bar,
We could enter a competition
And win a new car.

Oh pussy, pussy oh, how are you right?
Let's do go to the bar,
But then dance all the night.

Charlotte Elizabeth Bailey (9)
Finchale Primary School

Wonderful Puss

Oh pussy, oh pussy, you've never been fussy,
You came to me you beautiful pussy,
Oh pussy, oh pussy how pretty you are,
We could get insured and buy a car.

Oh pussy, oh pussy you are by far not a wussy,
Oh pussy, oh pussy I'm wrong you're right,
I've made a decision, let's never fight,
If you give me your hand,
We could join a band.

Jack Emberson (9)
Finchale Primary School

My Sister Danielle

My sister Danielle has ginger hair
And has a great big cuddly bear.
She likes to drive me round the bend
And Alice is her best friend.

Her favourite food is sponge cake,
All she does is stay awake.
She only plays with my toys,
The one things she hates is boys!

But at the end of the day she's my sister
And I love her.

Caitlin Neasham (9)
Finchale Primary School

The Zebra And The Giraffe

Oh what a charming zebra you are.
Your stripes are like a dark brown choco bar.
Let's travel in a car far far away
And let's stay there for a year and a day.
Oh yes, oh yes.
I will do it
And let's take a suitcase kit.
Let's write on lots of walls
And take lots of bouncy balls.
Let's get married,
How long have we tarried
And our wedding will be a big ball.

Alex Hendry (9)
Finchale Primary School

Canary

My canary is lovely, my canary is sweet
And the feathers give off very hot heat,
Your feathers are pretty don't you see?
How great is it to sing all day in a tree.
Your yellow feathers are bright as the sun,
Oh your tune is so lovely, it sounds like a hum.

Katya Chetina (9)
Finchale Primary School

Love

Love is the colour of red.
Love is like a soft heart.
Love tastes like sweet sausage.
Love feels like a fluffy cushion.
Love looks like my mam.
Love reminds me of when I was a baby.
Love smells like sweet fire.
Love sounds like birds tweeting.

Kate Appleton (7)
Finchale Primary School

Silence

Silence is white like my T-shirt.
Silence sounds like being on my own.
Silence looks like no one is there.
Silence feels like I am bored.
Silence tastes like a drink of water.
Silence smells like air.
Silence reminds me of having no friends.

James Borland (8)
Finchale Primary School

Fun

Fun is yellow like a bright sunny day
It tastes like a cold dripping ice cream
It sounds like a loud band of laughter
It looks like hopping and skipping in a circle
It feels like a really bouncy, bouncy castle
It smells like lots of juicy fresh air
It reminds me of my fantastic friends.

Katherine Bradshaw (7)
Finchale Primary School

Anger

Anger is red like a devil
It feels like a hot oven
It tastes like smoke in an engine
It reminds me of lava
It sounds like a volcano erupting
It looks like a hot rock.

Martin Briggs (7)
Finchale Primary School

Hunger

Hunger is the colour green like the cut grass.
It tastes like lovely food.
It looks like a big, fat juicy steak.
It smells like a cheesy pizza.
It feels like a tummyache.
It reminds you of the kitchen table.
It sounds like you're going to be sick.

Sarah Brown (7)
Finchale Primary School

Sadness

Sadness is blue like the sea
It tastes like water
It looks like tears
It smells like salt
It reminds me of two cars racing down my face
It feels like taps dripping
It sounds like someone crying.

Lewis Elliot Dawe (7)
Finchale Primary School

Darkness

Darkness is black like the dark corners of a dungeon
It feels like the black eye of a child falling over
It sounds like spooky ghosts coming up close
It reminds me of falling into a pond
It smells like horrible shadowy smoke
It looks like a black sky
It tastes like soggy paper.

Gradey Fairburn (7)
Finchale Primary School

Sadness

Sadness is blue like a tear.
It feels like no one likes me.
It reminds me of when no one liked me.
It tastes like salty tears.
It sounds like someone crying.
It smells like the hatred of everyone.
It looks like a giant tear.

Gavin Fraser (8)
Finchale Primary School

Silence

Silence is light blue
Silence is like the bright blue sky
It tastes like a juicy melon
It smells like a summery flower
It feels like a cute kitten
It reminds me of a purring cat
It sounds like the whistling wind.

Laura Greenley (8)
Finchale Primary School

Darkness

Darkness is black like midnight.
Darkness is like a charging rhino.
It smells like misty smoke.
It tastes like spicy mushrooms.
It looks like a googly-eyed witch's black cat.
It sounds like an angry fight.
It reminds me of the Grim Reaper.

Eleanor Griffin (8)
Finchale Primary School

Laughter

Laughter is green like growing grass.
It tastes like cold ice cream.
It sounds like a big happy smile.
It reminds me of lots of happy memories.
It smells like the warm sun.

Katie Harrington (8)
Finchale Primary School

Love

Love is pink like a big happy heart.
It reminds me of a handsome young man.
It sounds like beautiful love magic in the air.
It looks like a big, gigantic, peaceful Heaven of love.
It tastes like a big pink heart on a stick.
It feels like a ginormous pink feeling inside me.

Toni Hendry (8)
Finchale Primary School

Hunger

Hunger is red like a big juicy tomato
Hunger smells like sizzling sausages
Hunger tastes like yummy fruit
Hunger feels like a rumbly tummy
Hunger reminds me of yummy food
Hunger looks like fried eggs
Hunger sounds like baked potatoes being cooked.

Ellie Jayne Hopgood (8)
Finchale Primary School

Hate

Hate is the colour red like an angry little devil.
It smells like horrible black smoke.
It sounds like an erupting volcano.
It reminds me of the angry war.
It tastes like a burning fire.
It looks like a speeding missile falling from the sky.
It feels like a big bad wolf eating you up.

Ewan Loftus (7)
Finchale Primary School

Fun

Fun is yellow like the car.
It sounds like my car is racing.
It looks like my reading book.
It feels like a wet sponge.
It tastes like yummy pizza.
It smells like my mum's hairspray.
It reminds me of going to the beach.

Kqia Lomas (7)
Finchale Primary School

Love

Love is red, like a juicy red apple
It feels like light purple velvet
It smells like a bright rose
It reminds me of a round red heart
It tastes like a chocolate melting in my mouth
It sounds like a silent little mouse
It looks like a cuddly teddy bear.

Rebekah Lumsdon (8)
Finchale Primary School

Laughter

Laughter is blue like a little lying elf singing in the rain
Laughter is like a very hot fireball in my hands
Laughter feels like the rain in the night
Laughter smells like hot dog sausages
Laughter sounds like a big thunderstorm
Laughter reminds me of my grandma laughing
Laughter tastes like hot chocolate.

Georgia McCormick (8)
Finchale Primary School

Happiness

Happiness is gold like a shining sun.
It looks like a box of paints.
It feels like a silky kitten's fur.
It smells like a baked cake.
It sounds like children playing.
It tastes like a mini cream roll.
It reminds me of my holiday in Prague.

Freya Patterson (7)
Finchale Primary School

Silence

Silence is white like a scary ghost
It sounds like paper rattling
It smells like an empty air strip
It tastes like plain coloured rice
It reminds me of being quiet
It looks like fresh air
It feels like no one's there

Silence is yellow like the school's groovy chairs
It sounds like pencils being put in a pot
It smells like paper being photocopied
It tastes like eating an orange quietly
It reminds me of tiptoeing through the corridor
It looks like people jogging
It feels like I'm skipping quietly.

Isla Readman (7)
Finchale Primary School

Hate

Hate is the colour of cream skin
With tears running down.
It reminds me of when I was yelling
At my mum and she hated me.
Hate tastes like horrible stuff
Like mud and nobody likes mud.

Hate feels like you've been heartbroken.
Hate looks like you have fallen out
With somebody like your mum and dad
Or your best friend.

Jake Robson (7)
Finchale Primary School

Laughter

Laughter is green, like a field full of friends.
It tastes like a box of chips.
It sounds like someone laughing.
It feels like a feather tickling your nose.
It smells of sausage and mustard.
It looks like a clown throwing pies.
It reminds me of when I went to the circus.

Sven Lars Signer (7)
Finchale Primary School

Happiness

Happiness is red like a sweet strawberry
It reminds me of people smiling
It sounds like people laughing
It tastes like burger and buns
It smells like a lovely juicy orange in a fruit bowl
It looks like my mum
It feels like playing games.

Alex Thornton (7)
Finchale Primary School

Anger

Anger is red like an angry evil.
It sounds like a bubbling volcano.
It smells like a very hot fire.
It feels like my head's going to blow up.
It reminds me of hot peppers.
It looks like it's going to pop!
It tastes of chilli sauce.

Lucy Traynor (7)
Finchale Primary School

Hate

Hate is red like a raging volcano.
It looks like a burning fire.
It smells like steaming smoke coming from my mouth.
It sounds like someone shouting.
It tastes like horrible mashed onion.
It reminds me of someone being angry.
It feels like someone grabbing me.

Kaitlin Walton (7)
Finchale Primary School

Hunger

Hunger is green like a mint chocolate wrapper.
It sounds like the crunching of crisps.
It reminds me of long sausages and freezing ice cream.
It feels like chocolate melted on my hands.
It smells like burning burgers.
It looks like popcorn popping up and down.
It tastes like squashy mashed potato and round peas.

Benjamin White (8)
Finchale Primary School

The Night

Dream spreader,
Sunlight snatcher,
Peace scatterer,
Owl awakener,
Like a wizard cloak covering the sky,
The night . . .
The night . . .
The night . . .

Silver pearls,
Sparkling jewels,
Dust from Earth,
Glitter spreader,
Shimmering in the midnight sky,
The stars . . .
The stars . . .
The stars . . .

Silver bubble,
Giant's eye,
Dinner plate,
Glittery bobble,
Christmas bauble shining in the night sky,
The moon . . .
The moon . . .
The moon . . .

Lauren Wilcox (8)
Shotton Primary School

The Magic Box

(Based on 'Magic Box' by Kit Wright)

I will put in my box . . .
a tooth of dragon,
a hamster's tail
and the mouth of a worm.

I will put in my box . . .
a snail's antennae,
a tongue of a crocodile
and a snail's bone.

My box is fashioned from fish scales,
with red and gold stars and dinosaurs in the corners.
Its hinges are made from eyeballs.

Connor Simpson (8)
Shotton Primary School

The Night

Star sender,
Moon monster,
Sun banisher,
Speechless bat,
Sprawled on Earth like a hat,
The night . . .
The night . . .
The night . . .

Silver dust,
Lighted shape,
End of wand,
Shower of rain,
The stars . . .
The stars . . .
The stars . . .

Silver plate,
Giant's eye,
Face of man,
Silver ball
Rolling across space like a marble,
The moon . . .
The moon . . .
The moon . . .

Leigh Patterson (9)
Shotton Primary School

The Night

Dream seizer,
Nightmare seller,
Light disposer,
Black panther,
Like a wizard's cloak covering the Earth,
The night . . .
The night . . .
The night . . .

Monsters' eyes,
Quidditch balls,
Dust from Pluto,
Disco lights fired all over the sky
The stars . . .
The stars . . .
The stars . . .

James Seaton (9)
Shotton Primary School

The Night

Dream swifter,
Sunlight spreader,
Peace surrounder,
Glitter snatcher,
Gleaming in the midnight sky,
The stars . . .
The stars . . .
The stars . . .

Silver bubble,
Gloomy Earth,
Round football,
Silver coin,
Shooting around the Earth with a sparkle,
The moon . . .
The moon . . .
The moon . . .

Jennifer Scott (8)
Shotton Primary School

The Magic Box

(Based on 'Magic Box' by Kit Wright)

I will put in the box . . .
Five wishes spoken in Spanish,
A black sun
And a flying jellyfish.

I will put in the box . . .
A mermaid's toenail,
The smell of dinosaur's breath,
Michael Jackson slithering
And a slug dancing the moon walk.

My box is fashioned from ice, gold and steel,
With red stars on the lid
And dragon toes in the corners.
Its hinges are made from fish scales.

I shall swim in my box
On deep, blue ocean currents,
Then I will land onto a shore the colour of the sun.

Conor Willetts (9)
Shotton Primary School

The Night

Black bird,
Black blanket,
Black banner,
Black cap,
Black orb around the Earth,
The night . . .
The night . . .
The night . . .

Silver lemons,
Silver dots,
Shiny apples,
Silver footballs,
Silver diamonds floating in the dark sky,
The stars . . .
The stars . . .
The stars . . .

Craig Adey (9)
Shotton Primary School

The Night

Predator raiser,
Ebony cloak,
Star thrower,
Black bat,
A volcano erupting in space spewing out soot,
The night . . .
The night . . .
The night . . .

Silver shoe,
Beams of peace,
Gleams of dreams,
Beams of light,
Porthole for the beautiful stars,
The moon . . .
The moon . . .
The moon . . .

Smoke from Jupiter,
Ocean of diamonds,
Sprinkle of sequins,
Angels' shine,
Sharks shimmering in the deep blue sea,
The stars . . .
The stars . . .
The stars . . .

Ben Bowes (9)
Shotton Primary School

The Magic Box

(Based on 'Magic Box' by Kit Wright)

I will put in my box . . .
a sweet smell from a foot,
some sweat from a ghost
and a magic feather from an angel.

I will put in my box . . .
a shadow from a vile vampire,
a fifth week in the thirteen month
and a mermaid with shark's teeth.

My box is fashioned from multicoloured stars,
with rings on the lid and secrets curled in the corners.
Its hinges are made from witches' nails.

I shall fly in my box,
on the bright, cold moon,
then skip happily to the end of the day.

Brooke Darling (9)
Shotton Primary School

The Magic Box

(Based on 'Magic Box' by Kit Wright)

I will put in the box . . .
a green worm with big eyes,
a pot of gold from the end of the rainbow
and a ghost on a sunbed.

I will put in the box . . .
the smell of the seaside,
a hand from a mummy
and a phoenix's feather.

My box is fashioned from gold and silver jewels,
with ants' legs on the lid and secrets in the corners.
Its hinges are made from rotting fingernails.

I shall run in my box
up to Mount Everest,
then jump off it onto an undiscovered island.

Kyle Mark Addison (9)
Shotton Primary School

The Magic Box

(Based on 'Magic Box' by Kit Wright)

I will put into the box . . .
a pot of gold from the end of the rainbow,
blue clouds
and a squeak from a fish.

I will put in the box . . .
a boy with scales and a fish with a T-shirt,
a toenail from a ghost
and a mermaid's foot.

My box is fashioned from rubies,
with stars on the lid and diamonds in the corners.
Its hinges are cavemen's toes.

I shall ski in my box,
through twisting mountain paths,
then swoop onto an undiscovered country
with exotic bamboo trees.

Andrew Hughes (9)
Shotton Primary School

The Night

Dream snatcher,
Nightmare catcher,
Snore thrower,
Light stealer,
Covering the Earth like a black wizard's cloak,
The night . . .
The night . . .
The night . . .

Light burglar,
Star sender,
Witch's cloak,
Dust from Jupiter,
Like a hat covering the sun,
The night . . .
The night . . .
The night . . .

Giant's magnifying glass,
Shark's eye,
Dragon's watch,
Huge lamp,
Welcomes the planets and the stars,
The moon . . .
The moon . . .
The moon . . .

Silver football,
Frog's egg,
Gypsy's glass ball,
Welcomes the darkness with a beaming smile,
The moon . . .
The moon . . .
The moon . . .

Sophie Tracey Morton (9)
Shotton Primary School

The Night

Predator bringer,
Light banisher,
Black bringer,
Day shifter,
Like a black cat prowling in the sky,
The night . . .
The night . . .
The night . . .

Glittering pearls,
Dazzling dust,
Shimmering glitter,
Bright lights,
A shimmer in the night sky,
The stars . . .
The stars . . .
The stars . . .

Round plate,
Silver cloud,
White bird,
Metallic glass,
Like a sunflower beaming down on Earth,
The moon . . .
The moon . . .
The moon . . .

Kirbie Bestford (9)
Shotton Primary School

The Magic Box

(Based on 'Magic Box' by Kit Wright)

I will put in my box . . .
a purple star,
a horn from a unicorn
and a twinkle from a starfish.

I will put in my box . . .
Hallowe'en every week,
a black rainbow
and a mermaid's toe.

My box is fashioned from steel, stars and
the glow of the sun.
Its corners are filled with secrets and love.
Its hinges are made from dragon toes.

I shall surf in my box
on calm ocean waves,
then swim 10,000 miles until the end of the day.

Annalise Chandler (8)
Shotton Primary School

The Scottish Box

(Based on 'Magic Box' by Kit Wright)

I will put in the box . . .
the flame of the famous Buckbeak,
the spark from a sea unicorn
and a third Christmas.

I will put in the box . . .
blue moonlight,
a unicorn with a mane
and a lion with a horn.

My box is fashioned from shining stars
with a red rose on the lid and a baby's first smile in the corners.
Its hinges are made from ice fingers.

I shall swim in my box
in the deep blue ocean current,
then swim to the twisting mountain paths.

Rhiannon Prow (9)
Shotton Primary School

The Night

Dream dragger,
Nightmare scarer,
Predator's playtime,
Light snatcher,
Black bark,
Like a black cat prowling about
The night . . .
The night . . .
The night . . .

Sparkling spoon,
Exotic egg,
Silver saddle,
Silver shoe,
Space explorer's shining guide,
The moon . . .
The moon . . .
The moon . . .

Shiny sparks,
Dust from Neptune,
Sugar-coated chocolate,
Gleam in eye,
Like flames in the night sky,
The stars . . .
The stars . . .
The stars . . .

Shawnie Cushlow (8)
Shotton Primary School

The Night

Snore bringer,
Dream surfer,
Moon blower,
Fantasy sender,
Like olives have been scattered in the sky,
The night . . .
The night . . .
The night . . .

A silver tambourine,
A soup spoon,
Giant's plate,
A snowball,
Snowballs fired into the sky,
The moon . . .
The moon . . .
The moon . . .

Sam Musgrave (8)
Shotton Primary School

The Magic Box

(Based on 'Magic Box' by Kit Wright)

I will put in the box . . .
a tip of a unicorn's wing,
the reflection of a vampire
and a cry from a river.

I will put in the box . . .
the pot of gold from a sparkling rainbow,
the shout from a stone
and a fourth Christmas.

My box is fashioned from glittering rainbows,
with bright stars on the lids
and laughter in the corners.

I fly in my box
in the moonlight sky,
then land on an enchanted island.

Shannon Crawford (8)
Shotton Primary School

The Magic Box

(Based on 'Magic Box' by Kit Wright)

I will put in the box . . .
the scariest tarantula,
the pot of gold at the end of the rainbow
and a walking snowman.

My box is fashioned from secrets,
with a sting of a bee on the lid
and magic in the corners.
Its hinges are dinosaurs' claws.

I will fly to Africa in my box,
then buy lots of sweets and share them with Michael.

Craig Kitching (9)
Shotton Primary School

The Night

Sun banisher,
Dream bringer,
Black bat,
Nightmare maker,
Light hitter,
Giant's black head,
The night . . .
The night . . .
The night . . .

Moon bringer,
Star awakener,
Predator caller,
Champion snorer,
A long cloak around the Earth,
The night . . .
The night . . .
The night . . .

Five pence piece,
Torchlight bright,
Giant's head,
Star bringer,
Wave raiser in the night sky
The moon . . .
The moon . . .
The moon . . .

Dust from Mercury,
Flaming fire,
Scattered shells,
Spill of marbles,
Grand picture in the night sky,
The stars . . .
The stars . . .
The stars . . .

Michael Cooke (8)
Shotton Primary School

The Amazing Box

(Based on 'Magic Box' by Kit Wright)

I shall put in my box . ..
a dragon's fang,
a ghost's hair
and a goofy tooth from a mermaid.

I will put in my box . . .
a tarantula's wing,
an eyelash from a dolphin
and a rag doll's nail.

My box is fashioned from jewels with
diamonds and gold in the corners.
Its hinges are glass shoes.

I shall swim in my box
to the bottom of the ocean
and swim with sharks and dolphins.

Louise Williams (9)
Shotton Primary School

The Night

Dream spinner,
Light catcher,
Sleep spreader,
Peace stretcher,
Spreads a wizard's cloak around the Earth,
The night . . .
The night . . .
The night . . .

Silver plate,
Magic ball,
Round clock,
Sea commander,
Spreads a beam of light around the night,
The moon . . .
The moon . . .
The moon . . .

Sparkling pearls,
Dust from Pluto,
Christmas decorations,
Pencil points,
Disco balls that are shimmering in space,
The stars . . .
The stars . . .
The stars . . .

Rebecca Hutchinson (8)
Shotton Primary School

The Enchanted Box

(Based on 'Magic Box' by Kit Wright)

I will put in the box . . .
a snail singing Elvis Presley songs,
a toe from a mermaid
and a shoe from a sea horse.

I will put in the box . . .
an eighth day,
a black ghost sunbathing
and a crying stone.

My box is fashioned from silver and gold,
with shining yellow stars surrounded by a black sky on the lid
and a beautiful glow in the corners.
Its hinges are made from eagles' claws.

I shall dance in my box on a gigantic ship,
then I will sink to the bottom of the ocean
millions of light years away,
where the mermaids and the sea unicorns dance.

Jay Fleming (9)
Shotton Primary School

My Best Friend

Super, smart, sensitive and sweet,
My best friend is a special treat
And she is as wise as an owl,
But not as boastful as Simon Cowell!
Mean she's not and cool she is,
She's just the right best friend for me.
And she's as smart as a fox,
Because she writes books like Michael Cox.
Not as smart as smart can be,
But she knows the ABC.
The end of this poem is coming near,
Here she is with no fear
And finally she's won 'Best Friend of the Year'.

Danielle Kennedy (10)
Shotton Primary School

My Best Friend

My best friend is Chelse Dove,
She's cool and fun and full of love,
She likes to laugh, she likes to dance,
She likes to read and likes to write
And I know that because
She's my best friend Chelse Dove.

Charlotte Sanderson (11)
Shotton Primary School

Candy

I nspiring candy

L uscious lollies
O verall options
V agrant varieties
E verlasting eaters

C reamy caramel
A nxious Aeros
N utty jellies
D elicious delight
Y ucky and yum!

Sasha Ellis (11)
Shotton Primary School

Great White Shark

G rinding its teeth for food
R oaring with anger
E ating everything, everything's its prey
A ngry beast
T welve foot long

W hite tummy waiting
H ungry animal
I gnorant thing
T asting the flesh
E nding in bloody water

S harp razor teeth
H orrible beast
A nd very brainy
R ushing to the smell of blood
K iling its prey.

Lewis Willetts (11)
Shotton Primary School

Best Friends

B est thing ever
E nchanted feather
S tick together
T illy and Milly

F riendly and neat
R eally petite
I ntelligent mind
E nd of mine
N early divine
D isappear with love
S pecial friends with Heaven above.

Natalie Scott (10)
Shotton Primary School

The Things That Scare Me Most!

F ear the poisonous spider
E erie, slithery snakes
A lso the creepy floorboards get me spooked
R ats scratting on each other's tails

T errifying midnight moon
E mpty coffins in the gloom
R arrggh the skeletons shout out loud
R ustling of the trees
'O rrible vampires biting humans' necks,
R unning wild with freedom.

Calum Paul Hunter (11)
Shotton Primary School

My Best Friend!

M y best friend is very cool
A nd he is tall and never cruel
R eading about dinosaurs, zombies and stuff
T he good thing about him is he's very tough
I n a race he never comes last
N ever before because he's fast

C an never outrun him in a race
A nd he always flies ahead without a strain on his face
R unning home with his nose also runny
R iding around on bikes, he's always funny.

Adam Holmes (11)
Shotton Primary School

People

There are a lot of people
In the world
Old ones, young ones
Boys and girls

Each have best friends
And mums and dads
Some are good but some are bad

We all are special
In our own way
And try to make friends
For every new day

We all have feelings
that sometimes get hurt
But thank goodness for forgiveness
All over the world

Each and every one of us
Have someone who cares
Who we can count on and rely on
To always be there

The people who are special to me
Of course, would be . . .
. . . My family!

Rachel Hunt (10)
Shotton Primary School

Dogs

Dogs are cute,
Dogs are small,
Dogs are what I care about most of all.

Dogs are tall,
Dogs are slim,
At a dog show you must win.

Dogs are lovely,
Dogs are a godsend,
Dogs are your best friend.

Jordan-Nicole Armstrong (11)
Shotton Primary School

Athletes

Athletes are fast
Athletes are slow
Athletics players never say no.

Athletes are good
Athletes are not
Athletics players are really hot.

Athletes are cool
Athletes are fun
Athletes can do things, whether to jump or to run.

Hannah Loveless (10)
Shotton Primary School

Mythical Creatures

D ark heart,
R eckless claws,
A ngry eyes,
G roaning bones,
O dd head,
N asty fire

T errible
R aspberry fingers
O ld fingernails
L ittle nose
L ittle heart
S tinky breath

M oulting head
I ntelligent brain
N asty hooves
O dd breath
T iny teeth
A ll man from neck down
U pwards, all bull
R aging guardian

H airy feet
O ld as a tree
B elly the size of an elephant
B reath stinks
I diotic brain
T iny hands

M essy clothes
E vil face
D isgusting hands
U nusual features
S nake hair
A ngry attitude

G hastly ghoul
H orrible screaming
O dd voices
S cary faces
T errible dreams
S mall but deadly!

Dylan Lowes (10)
Shotton Primary School

Friendship

F riends forever
R iding together
I like you and you like me
E vil you might be
N ever
D isrespect you
S tay together
H olding hands
I like you and you like me, you are the
P erfect match for me.

Chloe Still (11)
Shotton Primary School

Dragons

D ragons
R aging things they are
A ll knights
G et chewed up into little parts
O scar the dragon is the winner
N o man will go near
S o stay away or you'll get chewed up just like them.

Nathan Hoyland (10)
Shotton Primary School

Football's Fab

F ootball's fab
O n the pitch
O ver the bar
T errible ref is a witch
B all is flat
A nd I scored a goal
L ike Wayne Rooney
L oopy ref has gone loony
S tupid mole has made a hole.

F ans are screaming
A nd I am dreaming,
B ut I love football.

Harry Winwood (11)
Shotton Primary School

Sports

Football's crazy,
Football's mad,
Football's loved by lots of lads,
                    (And lasses!)

Tennis is fast,
Tennis is great,
Tennis is your best mate.

Rugby is tough,
Rugby is hard,
Rugby players eat lots of lard.

Hockey sticks,
Hockey balls,
Hockey players are normally tall.

And just to sum it up,
Sports are what we love most of all.

Sam Cockroft (10)
Shotton Primary School

My Little Fat Pony

My little fat pony
Is cheeky and small,
He's anything but
Slim or tall!

He's sometimes grumpy
And bucks me off,
But he's my little fat pony
And I love him a lot!

Rebecca Bainton (11)
Shotton Primary School

A Feeling Poem

Love sounds like sweet music,
Love tastes like your favourite food,
Love smells like pure red roses,
Love reminds you of a soft flower bed,
Love looks like the way to freedom,
Love feels like the warm sun on your cheek.
Anger sounds like two big bass drums,
Anger tastes like red-hot chilli peppers,
Anger smells like black smoky air,
Anger reminds you of volcanoes erupting,
Anger looks like flaming fires,
Anger feels like you're stuck in the middle of nowhere.
Happiness sounds like birds chirping,
Happiness tastes like bubbles melting in your mouth,
Happiness smells like hot chicken cooking,
Happiness reminds you of your bed drifting,
Happiness looks like a stream of hot chocolate,
Happiness feels like the way to Heaven.
Hate sounds like blasting music,
Hate tastes like one-hundred-year-old rotting garlic,
Hate smells like fires burning,
Hate reminds you of your enemy coming for revenge,
Hate looks like a never-ending maze,
Hate feels like an undead soul creeping through you.
Fear sounds like a demolisher tearing down your house,
Fear tastes like poisonous drinks,
Far smells like a burning barn,
Fear reminds you of a horrible nightmare,
Fear looks like a bad dream in reality,
Fear feels like an eagle crushing you.

Alice Hall & Jordan Musgrove (10)
Shotton Primary School

Happiness 'N' Anger

Happiness sounds like birds singing sweet songs,
Happiness tastes like the best taste in the world,
Happiness smells like a big bunch of red roses in a beautiful garden,
Happiness reminds you of really nice things in your life,
Happiness looks like a grassy field of flowers,
Happiness feels like the best feeling you have ever felt.
Anger sounds like a big black hole swirling about roughly,
Anger tastes like red-hot chillies burning away in your mouth,
Anger smells like a pile of wood on fire with smoke around it,
Anger reminds me of a dark, stormy night,
Anger looks like a horrible stormy night,
Anger feels like a red-hot fire around you and won't go away.

Hannah Winwood (10)
Shotton Primary School

Feelings

A nger is like thunder in the stormy night,
N ight sky is whistling through fear,
G rounds flutter through wind passing,
E veryone feels the anger lifting fear
R ough volcanoes explode with fire.

H earts pester as some hearts cry,
A nger sets pestering people around,
T all fear strikes everyone,
E verybody hates something and that is hate.

Shannon Harris (10)
Shotton Primary School

Feelings

A nger feels like old tree bark,
N ever smells nice, more like smoke,
G reat thunder and lightning,
E nters my head that it is deep red,
R eminds me of fire.

F ear feels like the Arctic,
E ver smells like ice
A nd looks like a smooth ice cube,
R eminds me of sky-blue.

Jared Hind (10)
Shotton Primary School

Moods

Anger sounds like bombs exploding on the earth,
Anger smells like smoke floating in the midnight sky,
Anger reminds me of burning flames of fire,
Anger looks like lava from the death of the sky.

Happiness is like a diamond in the sky,
Happiness smells like flowers surrounding you,
Happiness reminds me of many happy times,
Happiness looks like laughter all around.

Sadness is like a ship on the stormy sea,
Sadness smells like sour fruit falling from the sky,
Sadness reminds me of a cat crying for help,
Sadness looks like fire from the pits of Hell.

Jessica Abbs (9)
Shotton Primary School

Anger

Anger looks like a blaze of fire,
Anger smells like dirty smoke in the air,
Anger tastes like sour sweets in your mouth,
Anger feels like trying to have a fight every day,
Anger sounds like bombs crashing to the ground,
Anger reminds me of people shouting at one another.

Ashleigh Rowell (9)
Shotton Primary School

How I Feel

Anger sounds like a banshee wailing in horror,
Anger tastes like scalding soup, the pain tearing you apart,
Anger smells like rotten eggs and mouldy cheese,
The smell drifting through the air.
It reminds me of pain, so horrifying it is hard to bear.
Anger looks like red as bright as it can get,
Like the colour of the Devil himself.

H eather reminds me of Scotland where I love the most,
A light in the darkness as warm as can be,
P eople saying hello on the gloomiest of days,
P olar bears, so cuddly, crunching through the snow,
I ce melting, dripping in a puddle,
N ightingales singing so sweet and gentle,
E legant fairies both brave and shy,
S ummer days so hot and bright,
S parkling wings on my fragile fairy friends.

Jade Stafford   (10)
Shotton Primary School

Love And Hate

Love sounds like peaceful music in your body,
Love tastes like someone kissing you,
Love smells like roses rising over your head,
Love reminds me of all the happy things that have happened to me,
Love looks like when you go on holiday,
Love feels like flowers made into a bed.

Hate sounds like your friends talking about you,
Hate tastes like bones,
Hate smells like burning aftershave,
Hate reminds me of your soul coming to tear you apart,
Hate looks like your future grave sitting in front of you,
Hate feels like your heart exploding into a thousand pieces.

Kieran Atkinson (9)
Shotton Primary School

Feelings

A nger sounds like football fans going crazy,
N ight storm frightening you in the night,
G et rid of your temper,
E verything smells like chilli peppers,
R ain coming down in a storm.

Love tastes like chocolate melting in your mouth,
Love sounds like a bird twittering in the trees,
Love feels like sweetness in your heart,
Love reminds you of kindness in your heart and body.

Sean Harvey (9)
Shotton Primary School

Happiness

H appiness feels like church bells ringing
A fter eating my wedding cake,
P laces to go to make cakes,
P lays music while we bake.
I n the park you see your lover,
N icely you hover over him,
E nds happily when you get your wishes,
S ends a letter to your heart,
S eems to make you happy.

Leah Winward (9)
Shotton Primary School

My Life

A long time since I was born,
Maybe on the Sunday morn,
Glowing bloom, some roses soon,
Looking like the glowing moon.
I was born with hazel eyes,
Born with deep love inside.
I don't like to boast and cry
Because I know that's weakness in your eyes,
'Cause loving you is all I want to do.
I am all alone now,
No one ever cares,
When I turn to talk,
No one's ever there.
Creations, relations,
Holding on to love,
Making friends,
Tying up loose ends,
On the other side of my life
If I could re-write,
I wouldn't change a thing
In my life.

Louise Carr (10)
Shotton Primary School

Happiness And Love

Happiness sounds like a bird's song in the sky,
Happiness tastes like chocolate in your mouth,
Happiness smells like sweet roses in a field,
Happiness reminds me of a cry of laughter,
Happiness looks like the sun blazing from the depths of space,
Happiness feels like a thing nothing can stop,
Love sounds like a heart beating.

Matthew Peart (10)
Shotton Primary School

Happiness And Sadness

Happiness sounds like rain pattering on the ground,
Happiness tastes like chocolate cake heading to go into my mouth,
Happiness smells like a breath of spring,
Happiness reminds me of my last birthday,
Happiness looks like purple bells in the garden,
Happiness feels like a touch of love.

Sadness sounds like people crying,
Sadness tastes like salty water poisoning me,
Sadness smells like a breath of hate,
Sadness reminds me of my grandad,
Sadness looks like blue tears dropping on the floor,
Sadness feels like a herd of animals trampling on you.

Jasmine Sanderson (9)
Shotton Primary School

Love

Love sounds like
Sweet birds singing in the sky.

Love tastes like
Home-made chocolate cake in my mouth.

Love smells like
Roses opening near me.

Love reminds me of
My family helping me.

Love looks like
A cloud reaching down from Heaven.

Love feels like
Someone hugging you.

Hannah Tones (9)
Shotton Primary School

Feelings

Anger is thunder in the stormy night,
Anger is chillies popping in your mouth,
Anger is hot smoke floating in the night sky,
Anger looks like ruby-red shining in the sun,
Anger feels like fire in your mouth.

Love sounds like birds in the tops of the trees,
Love tastes like chocolate softening on my lips,
Love smells like flowers growing in the garden,
Love feels like walking in a peaceful garden.

Emily Blenkinsopp (9)
Shotton Primary School

Feelings!

Anger sounds like lava erupting from a volcano
And throwing itself into the sandy desert.
Anger tastes of sour, red-hot chilli peppers burning your mouth.
Anger smells like sour, bitter lemon drops squashed beneath
your tongue.
Anger reminds me of frustration, annoyance
And when you can't do things alone.

Love sounds like the beating of two hearts beating as one,
Love tastes like the sweetest strawberry cheesecake pointing
in your direction,
Love smells like the sweetest fragrance and scent washing your
body with relaxation,
Love reminds me of doves flying down from the sky to greet you,
Love looks like a couple who are so joyful,
Love feels warm and soft as it wants to please you.

Danielle Bartram (10)
Shotton Primary School

Brands Hatch

Motorbikes scream and slide,
They fly like ducks skimming across the water.
As they skid round Paddock Hill bend,
They open their throttles,
Click up their gears
And squirt up the water on the hill,
Like scissors through paper.
They speed round Druids,
Slip up through their gearboxes
And fly down Graham Hill,
They turn the throttle ever so slightly
And screech down towards Surtees
And the last kilometres
Before the chequered flag is raised.
They have successfully completed the course!

Harry Day (10)
Startforth CE Primary School

The Motorbike

The engine groans,
The wheels whirl
As the motorbike clicks into gear
And chugs to a start.
It zips from here to there.
It's cold, but fast
As it splashes through puddles.
I skid to a stop in my driveway.
The dog comes charging for a walk.
She runs quickly by my bike,
Which goes fast like the wind.

Sandra-Lee Prewitt (11)
Startforth CE Primary School

Toaster

As the bread's pulled down, *spring!*
As it burns in the heat, *crack!*
As it gets ready to jump out, *jump!*
As it springs in the air, *ping!*
As the butter splatters into my hair, *splat!*
When I've eaten it up, *crunch!*
I want some more for my lunch, *yum!*

Ellen Ritchie (10)
Startforth CE Primary School

The Camera

It gets ready to flash
As it stares like an eye,
Dad anxious to have his photo taken
Puts on his tie.
Mum pushes the button,
Brother Tom trips over, *crash!*
Mum pushes the button
As he plunges into the pool, *splash!*
'Give us a smile,' Mum shouts
As Tom climbs out.
She clicks again, *flash!*
The family's holiday has begun.

Zoe Nicholson (10)
Startforth CE Primary School

The Mumbling Magic Machine

Buttons are clicking,
Click! Click!
Engines shudder,
Controllers rattle
Underneath the plastic tops.
The screen gleams.
Flash! Flash!
The fans groan
While whizzing around.
Sensors bleep.
Bleep! Bleep!
Wires vibrate,
Cogs twist and turn
As the rumbling, bumping,
Shocking magic machine
Roars into action
Doing what it has to do.
It flashes a million pictures
Onto the blank screen
As the owner comes home
And starts to be entertained!

Christopher Ridgway (10)
Startforth CE Primary School

Motorbikes

Vroom, vroom, speeding down the road I go,
Everybody else seems extremely slow.
I zoom down the motorway, going *bleep* and *fizz,*
The juicy diesel blasts me along with a whirr and a whizz.
Up the ramp at eighty-five miles I go,
I land with a thump and blend in with the flow.
I skid round the corner, spin carelessly round,
I click down to neutral and slide steadily across the ground.
Straight in front of me there has been a horrendous crash,
But I bounce over the police car and fly over the scene of the smash.
The police car hastily slips into top gear,
He charges blindly at me and shoot . . . splash off the end of the pier.
I softly cruise back home for a cup of tea,
With some oil for the bike and a chocolate biscuit just for me.

Christopher Wood (9)
Startforth CE Primary School

The Car

There was a car
Racing down the track,
Skidding around the corners.
The driver hit the horn in a moment of glee,
The co-pilot screamed above the noise of the engine,
'We're near the end,
We're going to be first!
Go right, then left.'
In a second they zoomed past the finishing line,
The man waved the chequered flag
And the crowd stood up and cheered.

Aaron North (11)
Startforth CE Primary School

The Ancient Television

The old box sounds all buzz, buzz, buzzy,
The picture changes to fuzz, fuzz, fuzzy.
As the presenters start to speak,
Every button begins to squeak.
As the news reporters decided to drearily drone on,
All the children moan and groan on.
Squeak, buzz, groan,
Speak, fuzz, moan,
Beep . . . beep . . . beep . . .
Bang!
Just as Grandma always said,
That hideous contraption is surely dead!

Emily Knox (11)
Startforth CE Primary School

Television

It once was black and white,
But now it's coloured bright
As a reflection in a crystal.
The remote control in the hands
Of an expert flicker,
Changes the programme quicker and quicker.
Every second there's a different channel
Screaming or whispering.

TV is amazing,
Getting better every day!
I'm sorry to say
Your programme is nearly finished.
Just one more zap
And it's done!

Jack Robinson (10)
Startforth CE Primary School

The Angelfish

Down beneath the depths of the dangerous dark ocean,
The beautiful, stripy angelfish dipped and dived about,
Dodging the hurtling pebbles as it daintily dipped downwards.
Suddenly danger loomed above,
Darkness overshadowed its rainbow-coloured body.
The fish twisted, turned, panicked and fled in terror!

Becky McKitton & Jaymie Hartley (11)
Startforth CE Primary School

Microwave

Fill the microwave
Clash! Bang!
Switch it on!
Tick-tock!
The door shuts.
Squeak! Squeak!
Slam!
The light switches on.
Clatter! Clang! Clash! Crunch!
The spinner shoots round and round,
Fizz! Pop! Ding!
Your quick, ready meal is waiting to be served.
Quickly! Collect your spoon from the drawer!
Rattle! Bang! Munch! Munch!
That's only breakfast!
What time is lunch?

Emilie Riley (10)
Startforth CE Primary School

The Amazing Pie Machine

The amazing machine in the
Extremely big barn was a pie machine,
An automatic pie machine
That worked day and night.
It made a clucking, squeaking sound
As it produced piles of pies.
Ring!
The steaming pies are golden and crispy
As they slide along the conveyor belt
And fall into the clean white boxes
That wait for them at the end.
Clank!
They slip to the side to be stamped.
Stacks of boxes stand like bricks in a huge wall
Waiting to be sent to the shops in a fleet of wagons.

Christopher Rutter (11)
Startforth CE Primary School

Windscreen Wipers

The wipers squeal
As they brush across the
Windscreen simultaneously,
Like synchronised skaters
On an ice rink.
The drops of water
Are pursued like runners
On a running track.
Suddenly the wipers are
Switched off and all you
Can hear is the vrooming
Of the engine.

Alex Doyle (10)
Startforth CE Primary School

The Tiger

The tiger prowls
Through the endless tapestry of thick, woven branches
Like a dog searching for its bone.
The tiger stops and stares,
Like an eagle searching for its prey.
He stalks through the green, gossiping grass,
His tummy tumbling, twisting and turning,
Until he can bear the pain inside him no longer.
He begins to growl, a ravenous roar.
Then . . . he pounces!

Emily Carey & Emily Kell (11)
Startforth CE Primary School

Night-Time

The dim light shines in the night.
It's quiet, as quiet as a ghost floating silently.
The misty moon haunts the midnight air,
Owls send signals to one another secretly
And the cold, circling wind whirling past
Defies me with its icy breath
And chases me down the silent street,
Deserted and cold.
I stand alone, haunted by the
Whispering in my ears.

James Harrison (11)
Startforth CE Primary School

The Toaster

The toaster pops and bangs at the end of the day
Making crispy toast ready for us when we come in from play,
Then it rests peacefully with not a sound,
Relaxing until we need another round.
Greedily we ask, 'Can we have another lot?'
'Yes!' replies Mum, as she scrapes more butter into the pot.
Then the poor old toaster has to start once more
To produce the scrumptious toast that we all adore.

Matthew Heron (10)
Startforth CE Primary School

The Bloody Battle

The bloody battle raged on, night and day.
Men fell screeching from the battlements
And the earth was soaked in blood.
The land was ablaze with flames.
Constant battle sounds and the screams of death
Echoed around the mournful mountains.
The battle blazed on.
The field was littered with the bodies of the dead.
Neither side had any mercy for the other.
As their weapons grew blunt,
Their anger and their urge to kill sharpened
And the battle raged on.

Fred Bowron (10)
Startforth CE Primary School

Forest

The forest is a wild crocodile,
Silent and still,
Waiting quietly for his fill.
With his snapping teeth and watery snout,
Beady eyes sensing about,
He lies calmly in the squidgy mud,
While he waits for something good.

But suddenly he turns angry
As he sees something tasty.
He gets more vicious
As the wind begins to rush,
Then his long, green, scaly body
Stops waving wildly.
Everything is calm again,
So quiet,
So quiet
As he sleeps.

Roy Stephenson (8)
Wingate Junior School

The Forest Storm

Giant and green the forest is quiet,
Not a creature to be seen.
Soft tweeting up in the trees,
Rustling of the leaves.

But the storm is coming,
The clouds are gathering.
The birds stop tweeting,
The wind blows angrily,
The long, wavy grass sways
While the rain splashes down,
                              Down,
                                  Down,
Until silence.
The rain drops off the
Green camouflaged grass.

Natalie Clish (8)
Wingate Junior School

To The Rhythm

Working hard at school
To the rhythm of the footsteps.
Slipping and running in PE
To the rhythm of the footsteps.
Solving maths problems
To the rhythm of the footsteps.
Kicking the football
To the rhythm of the footsteps.
Eating my dinner
To the rhythm of the footsteps.
Writing out poetry in my literacy book
To the rhythm of the footsteps.
Working out science problems
To the rhythm of the footsteps.
Playing in the playground
To the rhythm of the footsteps.
Picking out the best points
To the rhythm of the footsteps.
Doing what the teacher says
To the rhythm of the footsteps.

Jennifer Wilkinson (9)
Wingate Junior School

The Sea

I like the sound of the waves.
The sound of the waves is the voice of the seashells.
Also the sound of the blowing wind is the sound of waves.
It's the fancy song of the sea.

I like the wet sand.
When you stand on it, it sucks your feet.
Wet sand is like a sand hole,
It sucks you in and makes your heart beat.

I like the starfish
Lying on the rocks,
Like if it fell out of space,
From lying in the sky.

Adam Churchman (8)
Wingate Junior School

The Ocean

The cream soda of the sea,
Whooshing against patterned rocks,
Loving the sea song bouncing in my ears,
The smell of the sea salt.

The melted, cheesy sand pulling me down.
A golden carpet of syrup spread.
Grains hide in sand treasure.
The sand pulls you down.

The seagulls pinch my chips,
Shoo, shoo, the seagulls go by.
A horrible noise of seagulls.
Finally peace and quiet.

Jordan Bostock (8)
Wingate Junior School

The Sea

The sea is like sparkling jewels
In the silver moonlight.
It is a hungry dog
Playing in the fog.

Shells are like hidden pearls
Hiding a creature with a shiny coat
That sparkles in the sunlight.
If you disturb it, you might end up in a fight.

Jordanna Simpson (8)
Wingate Junior School

To The Rhythm

Working so hard at calculating numbers
To the rhythm of the teachers.
Playing with my friends
To the rhythm of the teachers.
Writing stories in literacy
To the rhythm of the teachers.
Doing comprehension with Mrs Sturrock
To the rhythm of the teachers.
Written maths problems with Mr Brown
To the rhythm of the teachers.
Discovering new things
To the rhythm of the teachers.
Working so hard
To the rhythm of the teachers.
Having spelling tests
To the rhythm of the teachers.
Learning to swim
To the rhythm of the teachers.
Investigating science
To the rhythm of the teachers.
At school
To the rhythm of the teachers.

Melissa O'Neill (8)
Wingate Junior School

The Sea Sounds

I like the noise of the shells,
It is beautiful, it is the sea.
I dream of being the sea,
Lovely to be.

The sea is like the sky,
Splashing everywhere,
Right in front of you,
So, so blue.

The shells are like shiny jewels
Sparkling in the sunlight,
Hiding in front of you,
Sinking in front of you.

Jason Robson (8)
Wingate Junior School

The Sea

Sand is like a carpet of gold
Glittering with sun,
Lying in front of your eyes
Under the cloudy sky.

The sea is like a gigantic wall.
It stays beyond the Earth forever.
The great pool of the Earth,
It runs with the wind and the waves curl up into a ball.

Shells are like diamond rocks,
They shine in the beam of the sun,
Hidden beyond the sand,
They shine in your hand.

Craig Whiting (9)
Wingate Junior School

The Sea

Sand is like a soft gold carpet
Glittering in the sunlight,
Lying down in front of you, in front of the sea,
It's sinking in my toes below me.

Shells are like hidden jewels, rich stuff
Hiding beyond the sand, they are a beautiful hidden coat.
The creatures inside are sleeping
In the cold, shivering sea.

Rocks are like bouncing balls
Rolling down the smooth sea
And soft beneath me,
Bumpy and wet behind me.

Shaunie Leigh (8)
Wingate Junior School

To The Rhythm

Playing with my friends
To the rhythm of the music.
Thinking so hard
To the rhythm of the music.
Reading my books
To the rhythm of the music.
Spelling day on Friday
To the rhythm of the music.
Literacy in the morning
To the rhythm of the music.
Running and jumping in PE
To the rhythm of the music - with my friend
To the rhythm of the music.

Daniel Healer (9)
Wingate Junior School

The Sea

I like the noise of the sea
Rushing to and fro.
I like the sound of the waves
Lashing on the stones.

I like the sound of the gulls
Calling down to Earth,
Looking at me always,
Flying in the air.

I like the sound of the shells
Clapping in the breeze,
In the glittering sunlight
Where I'd like to be.

Adam Presho (7)
Wingate Junior School

The Sea

Sand is like grains of gold
Shimmering in the sunlight,
Sometimes very cold and dark,
Ancient and old.

Rocks are like pieces of gravel,
Sharp, not soft but hard.
On the beach they lay
Waiting to be picked all day.

Waves are like a cold fire,
Licking and curving all day.
Sometimes like a bit of silk,
Almost as cold as milk.

Adam Leonard (8)
Wingate Junior School

To The Rhythm

Lining up to go inside
To the rhythm of the school bell.
Working hard at science experiments
To the rhythm of the school bell.
Working out maths problems
To the rhythm of the school bell.
Painting in art
To the rhythm of the school bell.
Eating sandwiches
To the rhythm of the school bell.
Giving out work
To the rhythm of the school bell.
Writing out stories
To the rhythm of the school bell.
Singing hymns
To the rhythm of the school bell.
Tidying up
To the rhythm of the school bell.
Going home
To the rhythm of the school bell.
Then doing homework
To the rhythm of the school bell.

Aimee Atkinson (9)
Wingate Junior School

To The Rhythm

Thinking so hard in lessons
To the rhythm of the school bell
Children painting art work
To the rhythm of the school bell.
Working out numeracy problems
To the rhythm of the school bell.
Kicking a football around in football
To the rhythm of the school bell.
Learning about Egyptians in history
To the rhythm of the school bell.
Typing up words in ICT
To the rhythm of the school bell.
Writing up wonderful poetry in literacy
To the rhythm of the school bell.
Learning about maps and mapping
To the rhythm of the school bell.
Throwing basketballs in the net
To the rhythm of the school bell.
Working so hard
To the rhythm of the school bell.
With the teachers
To the rhythm of the school bell.

Luke Catleugh (8)
Wingate Junior School

To The Rhythm

Laughing and chattering on morning play
To the rhythm of the school bell.
Scoring good goals too
To the rhythm of the school bell.
Writing poetry in English
To the rhythm of the school bell.
Typing away in fun ICT
To the rhythm of the school bell.
Getting your hands dirty in fun art
To the rhythm of the school bell.
Doing fun history projects
To the rhythm of the school bell.
Playing fun basketball
To the rhythm of the school bell.
Learning about maps and mapping
To the rhythm of the school bell.
Rolling about in PE
To the rhythm of the school bell.
Doing maths problems
To the rhythm of the school bell.
On my own
To the rhythm of the school bell.

Hannah Anderson (9)
Wingate Junior School

To The Rhythm

Running in the playground
To the rhythm of the school kids.
Working really hard
To the rhythm of the school kids.
Solving maths problems
To the rhythm of the school kids.
Painting messy pictures
To the rhythm of the school kids.
Finding science investigations
To the rhythm of the school kids.
Eating our scrummy dinners
To the rhythm of the school kids.
Writing out poetry
To the rhythm of the school kids.
Giving our work books
To the rhythm of the school kids.
Playing basketball outside
To the rhythm of the school kids.
Asking questions to the teachers
To the rhythm of the school kids.
Working on my own
To the rhythm of the school kids.

Charlotte Lamb (9)
Wingate Junior School

The Forest

The forest is a slithering snake,
Long and hissy.
In the grass he will *swish*.

The forest is a crocodile,
Long and vicious and green,
Flapping his tail wildly, so mean.

The forest is a city,
Long and loud,
People and animals in a crowd.

The forest is a book,
Big and green with things to find out
Hidden between green leaves.

Shane Jeffery (8)
Wingate Junior School

Crocodile

In the forest there's a calm crocodile,
Silent and still,
Waiting stealthily to frighten his prey,
With his green body and sweeping tail,
Hour upon hour he lies,
Eating the fish and bones, bones, bones.

But the beast goes wild. Suddenly the beast stops
And stares at his prey
With his sly eyes,
He smiles, viciously smirking,
Lurking nearer and nearer,
But the fear is getting much nearer.

The crocodile thinks very slyly,
While he's eating the animal like a pie,
Then he smiles like a fly.
The forest lets through the greenish scales,
The forest is a palace for a crocodile king.
Silent,
Silent,
The king lies.

Jack Fulton (9)
Wingate Junior School

The Forest

The forest is a cold city,
Big and dark,
The bins like long logs.
Cars go by, *beep, beep, beep,*
Like birds in the forest, *cheep, cheep, cheep.*
The leaves in the forest start to weep,
As winter brings the animals' long sleep.

The cold city is quiet.
The city gets fuller and fuller with crowds,
The trees start to roar
And the wind blows hard
And the people start to part.
Rain starts to fall
And the storm gets tall.
Trees start to roll.
So loud!
So loud!
They shout, 'The way in!'
Like animals.

Shannon Peacock (8)
Wingate Junior School

The Crocodile

In the forest is a calm crocodile,
Silent and slow,
Waiting patiently to get his foe.
With his green snout and staring eyes,
Sensing all around him, he lies
Camouflaged in the thick mud.
He looks for something that's good.

But suddenly he turns vicious
As he spies something delicious.
He snaps his jaws
As the trees begin to roar.
The branches fall,
He wants more,
He crunches his bones, bones, bones!

Brooklyn Bailey (9)
Wingate Junior School